PORTRAITS
FROM THE HUMAN FACES TOUR
Mental Health Struggles and Resilience

TED SWARTZ

WITH

VALERIE LUNA SERRELS

PHOTOGRAPHY

STEVEN STAUFFER

TED & COMPANY, HARRISONBURG, VIRGINIA

To those who have courageously shared their stories.

**1 in 5 adults in America
experience a mental illness.**
(NIMH)

**There is one death by suicide
in the US every 12 minutes.**
(CDC)

CONTENTS

NOTE: Statistics sourced from National Institute of Mental Health are credited as (NIMH) and those from the Centers for Disease Control and Prevention as (CDC)

Readers' Advisory

For those who might be sensitive to graphic depictions of
violence and/or trauma, we want to alert you to the intensity
and difficulty of many of these stories.

PREFACE

In 2012, I wrote a one-man play entitled *Laughter Is Sacred Space* as a way to process my grief after the suicide of my best friend and professional partner who had long struggled with bipolar disorder. Following performances, audience members would often approach me to share personal stories about their own struggles with mental illness or about losing someone close to them through suicide.

I was moved over and over again by achingly profound stories.

Their openness led to a special tour of the play in 2016, the "Human Faces Tour," which inspired this book. The tour was hosted in twenty-six cities across North America over a span of forty days. The play was performed as it had been for the previous four years, only now there was a new element. We wanted to capture the audiences' participation, so we provided sheets of paper and post-it notes for anyone to write down their stories after the performances. Some submitted their stories online at a later date.

Also, from the tour's inception, it felt important to include the individual faces behind those stories. We wanted to show the human face behind these struggles, the human face of resilience and strength. Trusted colleague and professional photographer Steven Stauffer accompanied us on that tour, offering audience members the opportunity to have their portrait taken after the show. While the photographs represent different age groups and genders, as a result of the specific venues that booked the play and who in the audience chose to participate, the portraits do not reflect the broad diversity we had hoped to include. It is important to recognize that mental health challenges affect all of us, regardless of age, gender, race, religion, or economic or social status as reflected in the statistics at the back of the book.

I will never forget the father who attended the show just weeks after his son had taken his own life. After the performance, the father left the church that was hosting the show that night. He drove home and then turned right around, driving the thirty minutes back to the church to talk to me. He needed to weep . . . and ultimately, just to be held.

There was also the older woman who approached me after the performance, holding a baby. I assumed she was the baby's grandmother. She introduced me to the baby girl and told me, "Her mother . . . my daughter . . . took her own life several months ago." I was humbled she felt comfortable coming to me to share her tragic story, and I was moved just to be in their presence.

There is something powerful that begins to happen when someone says, "tell me your story." It can be part of someone's healing, when they share and when we listen, and then maybe the listener will have the courage to tell their own.

You hold in your hands what emerged from that tour, and it would not be complete without including a heartfelt thank you to the many people, churches, organizations, and donors who made the Human Faces Tour successful. Thanks to the many hosts who booked the show—from Stephens City, Virginia, to Portland, Oregon—for opening your doors and hearts to our work and to this important topic, and for valuing the impact of the arts enough to invest time and money to bring live theater to your community. And a bow to those who gave generously to our Kickstarter campaign so we could get the tour on the road, and hire Steven and the crew. You are all our partners in shifting cultural norms to elicit more compassion, more acceptance, more love in the world. And for all the people whose faces and stories appear in this book, thank you for your courage to tell your own story and agreeing to make it public, for trusting us with it, and for the daily work you do to live out of your whole self. You are needed. This book is for you.

- Ted Swartz

x

Mental illness can affect anyone
regardless of culture, race, ethnicity,
gender or sexual orientation.

(NIMH)

Psychology: The science of mind and behavior
(Webster's Dictionary)

The word "psychology" was formed by combining the Greek word "psychē," meaning "breath, principle of life, soul," with the suffix "logia," which comes from the Greek word "logos," meaning "speech, dialogue, word, reason."

Another way to think of it:
Conversation of the Soul

A MATTER OF SOUL
HOW WE PERCEIVE PSYCHOLOGICAL CONDITIONS

VALERIE LUNA SERRELS
PROGRAM DIRECTOR AND AGENT, TED & COMPANY THEATERWORKS

We are born into a soul that is whole, unique, and sacred. Yet it does not take long for difficult or traumatic life experiences, or a triggered inherited tendency to lead us away from that truth. Over time, these challenges can establish behavioral patterns that can seem impossible to control or change. These patterns can become maladaptive, keeping us stuck in painful mental and emotional spirals. Eventually, these patterns may lead to recurring difficulties with relationships, school, or jobs, deteriorating how we perceive ourselves, others, and the world around us. For some, these entrenched patterns become chronic and overpowering, and can lead to thoughts of suicide and, too often, completed suicide.

Statistics on suicide and mental disorders are disquieting, especially the 50 percent increase in suicide among girls and women and the 30 percent increase overall during the past two decades.[1] This is a red flag, a wake-up call. Although the availability and use of medications for psychiatric disorders has exploded over the past few decades, statistics suggest that treatment solely based on the dominant medical paradigm may be inadequate to address our mental health crisis, and often can create more problems.

Humans have long explored the soul, spirit, and mind, studying what drives behavior and the interconnection of invisible psyche and material body. The intersection of spirituality and science within the modern fields of psychology and psychiatry led to an ongoing debate from the beginning, with Sigmund Freud shaping a biologically centered approach to mental disorders, and Carl Jung shaping a soul-centered approach.

The neurobiological approach (from the Freudian tradition) is predominant today. As vital as this approach can be in treating serious mental illness, it often dismisses other aspects of the whole human person. Fortunately, many mental health professionals have also been influenced by Jung, who believed in the importance of understanding the soul, the true Self, as integral to healing. Yet an approach that recognizes the soul is still heavily overshadowed by a reliance on pharmaceuticals to fix, or sedate, what is determined to be a purely physical problem.

The dominance of the medical approach has led to a myopic view that minimizes the psychospiritual dimensions of what psychiatry has termed mental illness. When a system is not informed by the interconnectedness of all of its parts, it is ineffective at achieving its purpose. Some professionals within the mental healthcare system are addressing the duality of a neurobiological approach devoid of soul and context, reorienting toward understanding and treating the full person that includes the soul as well as the body, in addition to the cultural, environmental and ecological impacts on human well-being. Such an integration is critical.

This book is our small attempt to offer the reader a lens through which to recognize the whole person—body, soul, and spirit—keeping in mind that every life is influenced differently via the ancestral, environmental, and sociopolitical realities in which they live. Through portraits and personal stories, we are led down dark hallways of personal experiences and through hopeful landscapes of growth and resilience. All who were brave enough to contribute their stories or sit for a portrait have lived in vivid proximity to the complexity of the psyche. Many have sought help from the mental healthcare system.

Stepping into that world of psychologists and psychiatrists, diagnoses and labels, can be a formidable challenge. While some may be relieved to find out what is "wrong" with them or with a loved one, others openly rebel at being placed in a tidy box created by a label. Even though the message is often given that "you are not the label," a sense of shame, or feeling "broken" or "abnormal" can persist even after a psychiatric diagnosis. These feelings and beliefs perpetuate a fixed mindset that often further distances us from our soul.

And yet these perceived "broken" places are often the doorways into further growth and maturity. We are more than the difficult circumstances, emotions, or psychological crises we may experience. Our true identity lies much deeper, within our soul. Tightly held beliefs about our brokenness can shift when we begin to see ourselves, and one another, from this place, our true Self, allowing us to embrace the complexity of being whole and fully human.

Without this shift, we can remain stuck in feelings of shame, preventing us from seeking help. Family members or close friends can also feel embarrassment or shame about our condition, adding to the problem. In fact, a global study found that people tend to be more embarrassed by family members who suffer from a mental health diagnosis than those who suffer from a physical health condition.[2] Sometimes fear guides reactions to those perceived as different or troubled, especially regarding "mental illness." Misconceptions abound, perpetuated by movies, jokes, and sensational news, leading to stereotyping, prejudice, and discrimination. We can all be part of breaking this cycle of misinformation and stigma by challenging the stereotypes we hear and looking deeper.

As we encounter psychological symptoms of what we have come to know as mental illness, either within ourselves or others, perhaps we should consider dropping labels. Instead of pathology, we can see symptoms that arise as a natural response to ancestral, developmental, and environmental pressure leading toward wholeness and maturity. And maybe then we can begin to know ourselves and others through a different lens—in the light of our own or another's true wholeness and essence.

A friend who is a psychotherapist specializing in trauma believes that the true Self, or soul, within each of her clients is whole, has never been broken, and is waiting for them to come back home. Often it is difficult for a person suffering a psychological crisis to believe this. She tells them that it is her job as a therapist to hold the belief for them until they sense and trust their own courage and compassion to believe it for themselves. Perhaps even we, as laypeople, can also hold this belief for others, as well as for ourselves.

We can remember that no person is exempt from psychological challenges—whether unobtrusive or destructive—regardless of social standing, income, age, gender, intelligence, or ethnicity. Most who have been diagnosed with depression, anxiety, or other psychological disorders are productive members of society, people we meet every day—our teachers, store clerks, bankers, doctors, pastors, and janitors. While some may not be as "productive" in jobs or careers, this does not mean they are less human, or less whole at the deepest level of soul, than the most highly functioning among us. Often, these people have much wisdom to offer, having learned valuable lessons through suffering or difficult life passages.

Once we are truly open to "see" another person, beyond labels or exteriors, without judgment or fear, we may catch a glimpse of soul, and recognize our shared humanity and spiritual belonging. At the heart of most religious traditions is the reminder of our ultimate unity. We are all connected with one another, with the Creator, and with all life. The photographs and stories included on the following pages invite us to remember this.

You will encounter stunning, intimate portraits of people who have suffered, or suffer still, from the sometimes overwhelming challenges of living through a crisis of soul, and the potential stigma and isolation of a psychological diagnosis. These faces and stories invite you to see into the sacred essence of an individual behind a label, to meet each featured person on a deeper level. Through Steven's intuitive eye, we discover both struggle and hope in the tilt of a chin, the gaze of the eyes, a half smile. Some who sat for portraits also shared their stories, but there are also stories not accompanied by portraits as well as stories from those who wished to remain anonymous. You will discover stories that are both personal and universal.

This book is offered with hope and remembrance and with great respect for the millions of us who face incredible challenges to recollect the essence of who and what we truly are. It is an invitation to walk ourselves and one another back home into our wholeness, despite labels or the heavy burdens we might carry. It is a call to remember what we are at the deepest level—embodied souls with the incredible power of resilience, compassion, courage, and love.

1   Winerman, Lea. "By the Numbers: An Alarming Rise in Suicide." *American Psychological Association.* January 2019, Vol. 50, No. 1. Accessed August 2019. https://www.apa.org/monitor/2019/01/numbers.

2   Ahmedani, B. K., et al. (2013). "Embarrassment when illness strikes a close relative: A world mental health survey consortium multi-site study." *Psychological Medicine,* 43(10), 2191-2202. DOI: 10.1017/S003329171200298X. Accessed online August 2019. https://www.ncbi.nlm.nih.gov/pmc/articles/PMC4013530/.

Stigma harms the 1 in 5 Americans
affected by mental health conditions.
It shames them into silence and
prevents them from seeking help.
(NIMH)

Photo by Wayne Gehman

FINDING A WAY HOME
EMBRACING GRIEF THROUGH LAUGHTER

TED SWARTZ

Actor, Playwright, and Creative Director
Ted & Company TheaterWorks

Five years after a devastating loss, I wrote *Laughter Is Sacred Space*. The play is based on:

> a published memoir,
> a shared experience,
> a true story,
> laughter,
> and the start of a friendship.

The friendship was with Lee Eshleman, who was my creative partner for almost twenty years. We were inseparable in people's minds—Ted and Lee, the comedy duo, a tidy brand, three letters in each name. We were an acting company that created original works and toured theaters, colleges, high schools, and churches. A number of our plays were based on biblical stories, in which we explored what was funny within them. We believed laughter and humor to be the quickest path to the humanness of these stories, even a serious one. When we laugh with one another, perhaps about a shared misunderstanding, or when we recognize absurd truths about ourselves, we celebrate our shared humanity. When that laughter is wrapped around a sacred text, it opens up that text and, I believe, draws us nearer to the Creator. Laughter is sacred space, after all.

Ted and Lee TheaterWorks was full-time work in the performing arts—a labor of love, sweat, and determination.

It was our calling—together—until Lee ended his own life. Suicide.

Before Lee's death I was unaware that the terms we use to describe or identify suicide have evolved. I used the combined words "committed suicide," not knowing that the roots of the phrase are a holdover from a time when suicide was considered a criminal or a sinful act. We commit sins; we commit crimes. The sensibility around suicide today is more grace-filled, and certainly criminality is no longer an element. Suicide as a sin is a bit more stubborn, but, thankfully, that notion is also slipping into disuse.

As with most phrases or terms that have a long and strong cultural history, separating "committed" from "suicide" requires practice. With this in mind, here are a number of phrases to try:

> taking one's own life
> dying by suicide
> ended their life
> completed suicide

On the morning of May 17, 2007, at a high school in our hometown in Virginia we loaded in a show for a short run of our newest production, *Live at Jacob's Ladder*. We built the set, placed the props, rehearsed the entrances and exits—often the most difficult cues to remember—and did a speed run of the most troublesome script points.

Sometime after our lunch business meeting and before the check-in with the third performer at 7:30, Lee stopped fighting his decades-long battle with depression and ended his life.

Opposite page: Ted, with Lee's trademark yellow sneakers.

On that Thursday afternoon I lost my creative partner, writing partner, acting partner, company graphic designer, product manager, copy editor, travel companion, business partner . . . and my best friend.

I had met Lee through a theatrical emergency. I was a nontraditional first-year college student at the time (thirty years old, married with three kids) with a small reputation as a comedy actor. I had been asked to perform some funny stuff to be sprinkled throughout the programming at a three-day youth leaders' retreat at a camp in Pennsylvania. I created material based on the Spanish Inquisition sketch by Monty Python (always steal from the best), asked a young actor I knew to work with me, rehearsed the material, and eagerly anticipated our time onstage. We were to leave on Friday, but on that Monday, my co-actor called and said he had a last-minute rehearsal of the fall college theater production and now couldn't go to Pennsylvania.

I spent Tuesday and Wednesday looking for anyone with interest and ability, and right about the time I was ready to drop the ability and just go with interest, I ran into my old friend Joe, the president of the university I was attending. As a joke, I asked him if he could fill in. (Fine president, but as an actor? . . . He's a fine president.) He said no, but he asked that auspicious question, "What about Lee Eshleman?"

"That'd be great," I said, "He's funny, but I don't know him personally."

"I'll introduce you," Joe offered.

Lee was working in the university print shop. We walked in, and Joe said, "Lee, this is Ted. Ted, this is Lee. I think you have something to talk about." And then he left me there with a startled look on my face.

"Hi there," I said, "you don't know me, but I've seen you perform . . . you were funny . . . and I was wondering if you wanted to go away with me this weekend?

"Yes, this weekend . . . and perform some comedy bits. There's no money in it, but it's a beautiful camp, and there is a very good chance we'll have fun."

Despite an admittedly cautious nature, Lee agreed to go; he later said it was the hungry desperation in my face that convinced him to do so.

We left as originally scheduled on Friday and performed our first sketch together on Saturday. After our performance, most people in attendance thought we had been working together for years, although we had met just three days before. This wonderful happy accident (I never did work with that other actor again) began a close friendship and professional partnership based on the delicious premise of making people laugh.

I had discovered my comedic soul mate. We had an almost identical appreciation for what was funny but different and complementary ways to get there. Lee was a brilliant wordsmith, a summa cum laude college grad with the soul of a class clown. Even though I was seven years older, I had just started college, didn't know how to spell "come louder," and was the concept writer who wrote minimalist physical pieces that depended on facial expressions and lots of falling down.

As we learned from each other, my vocabulary grew richer, I learned the value of diction and punctuation, and Lee expanded his appreciation of physical comedy. We learned to negotiate our faults and idiosyncrasies and how to disagree.

Lee was also an introvert and perfectionist, whose first impulse to a new idea was to determine why it wouldn't work. I am an extrovert, addicted to the next fun idea, sometimes to the detriment of the current project. It was our biggest point of conflict, and we didn't always do a good job of hashing out those differences.

But, it was our calling, and we found a way through. So, negotiation, appreciation, anger, learning from each other, navigating highs and lows, and a naive persistence to stay together, kept us together. Hmmm, sounds like a marriage. Just without the vows and some other good things.

I remember thinking . . . Wow, this is more fun than I thought possible, maybe more fun than sex, or baseball, even.

We would have almost twenty years together.

Laughter Is Sacred Space was my way to process the unfathomable, an attempt to give meaning to tragedy.

In time I have come to recognize that any healing I can claim is tied forever to the show, in particular:

> The creating and writing of the play with director Ingrid De Sanctis (who was also processing her own grief);

> The first stumbling performance for my and Lee's own congregation at a church retreat, where the emotions were raw and shared grief a welcome release;

> The touring, when people across the country helped me better understand the impact of the vulnerability and honesty I was able to bring to each performance.

The need to create and the need to get back onstage pushed me to confront my deep anger, grief, and guilt, and to move forward . . . or just move.

The audiences helped me do that. What I've learned in this angst-filled thrill ride of a career in theater is how the energy of an audience can be a never-ending source of power and support. I know that each show's audience is there primarily to be entertained, but I also believe they have come with the expectation that they will learn something and perhaps be moved.

Touring *Laughter Is Sacred Space* has been a sacred journey. Audiences who came to see the show were especially engaged. Their focus was sharp, and I could feel their energy. It was often palpable and manifested in laughter, an intake of breath, or delicious silences. After the performances, people would often come up to me and share their own personal stories of struggle with mental illness, or of losing a loved one to suicide. Some invisible door opened to allow for this kind of human connection. It was so powerful that after three years the idea developed to run a special tour to provide space for audience members to share their experiences.

In September 2016, stagehand Dietrich Alderfer, photographer Steven Stauffer, and I loaded a van with props, set pieces, Epsom salts, ibuprofen, and snacks. We strapped lighting poles and three ten-foot ladders to the roof and jammed our suitcases into the remaining crannies of the company's full-sized Chevy Express. We set off for a month-and-a-half-long tour. Forty days, twenty-six shows, twenty-six different cities, towns, villages, hamlets, burgs, and everything in between.

Oh, and then, just to raise the stakes, we had the money to set out but not enough to get back home, so we started a crowdsourcing campaign the day we left. (By the way, I don't recommend this.) As the tour progressed, our excitement over people's generosity was too often tempered by the anxiety of watching the total raised move excruciatingly slow on most days. We began filming videos entitled *Get Steven Home* that showed our photographer trudging down a dusty road in Kansas, perched on a mountaintop in Colorado, or emerging from a cornfield in Iowa, looking lost and bewildered, wondering if Brooklyn, New York, would ever see his lanky frame again. In a rush of stress-inducing last-minute contributions, we reached our goal. Steven made it home. (Along with the rest of us.)

I have spoken to and performed for thousands in the United States, Canada, and England, about grief, pain, mental illness, and mental health. My own healing has been tremendously impacted by the response of audiences and by individuals who share their own stories. Many of those opportunities have come in churches. In the play, I describe churches as "well-positioned, too often ill-informed followers of Jesus who too often hide our weaknesses and vulnerabilities and confuse mental health with spiritual health." I believe this to still be true, but we are making headway. I am encouraged by the strong movement of many churches and also of our culture to start talking more about mental illness and mental health.

I hope that each performance of *Laughter Is Sacred Space* casts a little more light into the shadows where mental illness resides in this culture; that the performances celebrate the lives and hearts of those who persevere and also those who lose their lives to mental illness. I still miss Lee dearly, and I am humbled and deeply moved by the opportunity to tell our shared story and hear hundreds of stories of grief and resilience in return. When we discuss difficult topics openly, we destigmatize them. Mental illness is certainly one of those conversations.

I hope and pray this continues to be so. The shared health and well-being of our communities depend on it.

EXCERPTS AND REFLECTIONS FROM THE PLAY
LAUGHTER IS SACRED SPACE

PLAYWRIGHT, TED SWARTZ

DEPRESSION WITH A CAPITAL "D"

Laughter Is Sacred Space: Act I, Scene 2

"It didn't take long after meeting Lee that I began to witness what bipolar disorder looked like, although it would be another few years before he would be diagnosed. It scared the hell out of me. I suppose I gradually became used to his spikes of wonder and creative ideas, but sometimes those manic stages—when his excessive energy and creativity were just a little scary—made me wonder just who this man disguised as my friend was.

And the other side of the manic?

We've all been down . . . discouraged. I call this depression with a lowercase 'd.'

Lee had a different kind.

His was a way of life, a monster lurking not just under the bed, but around every corner. A constant companion. The demon that sits on your shoulder and whispers in your ear, telling you what you can't do, what you can't be, what you'll never become. That depression earns the capital 'D.'

In those early years I didn't know bipolar was what Lee had.

What I did know was my friend could alternately move the world with his creative genius one day and the next be unable to get out of bed and simply function as a human being. It was terrifying."

GRIEF *Laughter Is Sacred Space*: Act II, Scene 2

"It's been said that mourning is an action . . . it's intentional. It can and should be a conscious decision to mourn. Grief is different; grief just happens. I chose the 'brilliant' option not to mourn and to fight the grief. The problem was that I was doing battle with an opponent I couldn't see and couldn't find. Grief is like a shape shifter. You never know what form it will take, and you never know when it will show up.

So how do you battle grief? You first deny its existence. You try and convince yourself it didn't matter so much, that you really didn't care so much; it wasn't possible to love someone that much.

A bit like slapping on cheap low-grade drywall to hide the rotting timbers underneath, or throwing a rancid piece of meat behind the couch and hoping no one notices."

DREAMS *Laughter Is Sacred Space*: Act II, Scene 1

"In response to trauma many of us dream. In this one particular dream following Lee's death, we're cleaning up after a show, like we had done thousands of times. Lee was in charge of the props, I took care of the sound system. The rhythms were familiar, the adrenaline holding off fatigue. It felt like home . . . that space on and around the stage.

But, this dream was very strange as we both know it's a dream; we both know he's dead.

'I really like the new projects you're working on,' he says.
'Thanks, it would be more fun if I was doing them with you,' I say.
'Then you should have done more to help me.'
'Is that why you gave me the ultimate middle finger?'

I wake up.

You should have done more to help me. I thought I had. I worked around it, under it, despite it. I really thought I had.

Maybe he was right. Maybe I didn't really know how to help. Suicide wasn't even a possibility in my mind. This wasn't part of the plan. "

SERIOUS THOUGHTS ON LAUGHTER

I have spent thirty years studying why we laugh and implementing what I discover on stage. Studying comedy is a bit like dissecting a frog. You learn a great deal about the frog, but the frog is now dead. Too much analysis kills the comedy.

Laughter and comedy are subjective and vary wildly across cultural, racial, and geographic lines—except flatulence, which apparently crosses most of these lines.

When you laugh, you are healthier; you have more oxygen in your blood system; your body and your mind are more open. When your body and mind are more open, your heart is more open.

There are probably more reasons why we laugh, but we often laugh:

> when we are surprised,
> when we are delighted,
> when we recognize truth,
> and when we recognize ourselves.

Within *Laughter Is Sacred Space* are a number of moments of surprising laughter. This was one of my favorites:

> " One of the responses to Lee's death that pissed me off was the assumption that my career was over, that without Lee, why or how would I go on:
>
> [*Me speaking to an unseen person*]
> 'What do you mean, what am I going to do now?'
>
> 'Well, without Lee . . . I mean, he was your muse, you were the straight man to his wacky characters.'
>
> 'Straight man?! Straight man?!! Have you watched anything we've done in the last 10 years?!'
>
> 'Well, I just assumed you would do something else.'
>
> 'Like what?!'
>
> 'Go back to school, or teach . . . take a pastorate.'
>
> 'Take a pastorate? Oh that would be smart, take an angry wounded man and put him in charge of a congregation . . . [*aside to audience*] That's never been done before.' "

It was this last little aside when laughter would often explode. The audience, usually a churched audience, would recognize the painful truth of what too often happens in our congregations. These moments of laughter serve as a relief from the growing seriousness and vulnerability revealed in the play.

THE PHOTOGRAPHER'S PERSPECTIVE

STEVEN STAUFFER

On the night of the first show of this tour, Ted and Valerie and I had no idea how this concept would play out. Have an audience watch a very personal and emotional account of Ted's experience with Lee's death, and then have them volunteer to have their photo taken under a big light and share their own stories of coping with mental health issues? We didn't exactly expect the line to wrap around the block.

And yet out of the 150 or so in the crowd that first night, five people volunteered to share their story and have a portrait made. (That was about five times the number we had cautiously hoped for.) And night after night, a handful of people from each of these communities across North America were willing to stand under that light, look down the barrel of the lens, and tell us about their experiences, both through words and the expressions on their faces.

These portraits show people at a variety of points in their journey with mental illness. Some are grappling with it in the immediate present, with open wounds. For others, agreeing to have their portrait taken is an acknowledgement of something they're starting to come to terms with. In contrast, some seem quite comfortable in their skin, veterans of their own battles, open to discussion of their issues and even eager to share. Others are caretakers or loved ones of someone with a mental illness, and more often than not you can see in their eyes that they carry their loved one's pain with them.

Over the course of several months, some wrote pages and pages of their story through an internet link or email to the office, recounting personal experiences, reflecting on hope lost, hope gained. Others simply shared a few words. On the first night of the tour, one person who stepped in for a portrait, Lisa, wrote of her own diagnosis and shared it with me:

> "Others have made up a word . . . bipolar. All I know is that I feel things deeply."

Above all else, that's what I witnessed on this tour. Things felt deeply. Deep pain, deep joy. Deep ambivalence, deep certainty. Deep loss, deep hope.

We wanted to keep the photographic elements as consistent as possible among the portraits to keep the focus on the people themselves. With the background, lighting, and black-and-white edit staying the same throughout, all the variety is in their faces. We're able to see nuances. Not all smiles are alike; not all smiles mean the same thing.

Regardless of where they were on their journey, after every portrait session, I was left humbled by everyone's vulnerability, their willingness to share something so personal, and I hope their stories and images resonate with anyone who picks up this book.

Opposite page: Steven (right), with Ted during the tour

IF WE HAVE THE COURAGE to tell our story, *and* if we have the courage and grace to listen to the stories of others, we can, in heart-led ways, change a small part of the world.

PORTRAITS AND STORIES
from the HUMAN FACES TOUR

"I AM SOMETIMES ASKED when my depression and anxiety began and when it ended. Neither point in time can be identified. It is like humidity in the air. Sometimes it is wetter than others and I do not know where the water first originated.

There is no easy shelter to construct against this moisture. The work is wearisome and tiring. It is often filled with doubt. But it also contains moments of transcendence and tranquility. These are times when I accept reality. When I see that I do not have to define myself by my diagnosis. When I know I can accomplish all that I want to accomplish in spite of the rain, or mist, or fog."

- JOSHUA

"I HAVE LOST DEAR FRIENDS to suicide. I have had suicidal feelings myself. I deal with and have been affected by addiction. My faith and my relationship with my higher power are key to my serenity and health. Being part of a very supportive fellowship with others who struggle and use the twelve steps of AA to learn how to live life has been and is a steadying force. Therapy and medication can also be helpful sources for mental health.

I remember one evening feeling that I did not want to be alive. I was crying and praying at the same time. I heard my higher power tell me clearly, 'Don't hurt yourself, get up, take care of yourself, and don't take those other people's stuff on yourself.' So that's what I did. This is a daily walk. I have not found any magic answers."

- MARY KAY

KIM

BARB

"WHEN I WAS THIRTEEN YEARS OLD I was seriously depressed, to the point of contemplating suicide. I had no friends, my parents were never home, I was alone. As time went on, I became self-destructive, which led to more self-loathing. In mid-May of 2012, I decided to commit suicide. I put on some music and grabbed the gun that always sat on the night table. The lyrics of a song seeped in and stopped me. Music saved my life."

- ANONYMOUS

"ON THE NIGHT that I came to see *Laughter Is Sacred Space*, I was in a particularly vulnerable state, as it was the same day I had been officially diagnosed with generalized anxiety disorder, as well as showing symptoms of secondary depression and obsessive compulsive disorder. Hearing this as a university student only recently acquainted with the independence of adulthood was hard-hitting. I felt terribly alone, with nothing but my cocktail of destructive symptoms.

In brief, my anxiety and all its cronies create intrusive thoughts that urge me to tidy myself away in a corner of the room without a trace so as not to burden others with my presence. These are vicious doubts that often supersede logic.

For a long time I didn't feel credible enough to share my story with the world, as someone with an ongoing battle against mental illness. On some days I win, and others I lose. The reality for myself, as well as for many others, is that the cumbersome journey toward better mental health may very well be continuous. My mental illnesses aren't conquerable entities, nor are they dragons to be slain. Instead, I like to compare them to apathetic housemates who steal serotonin from the fridge and refuse to pay rent. You're damned to an eternal tenancy agreement that, at first, feels unmanageable.

I am so happy to share that I am now in the process of recovery. Opening up about my mental health, granting others access to the inner workings of my mind, has allowed me to regain autonomy over my life. When you lose your grip on rationality in your internal monologue, you need others to turn to as an anchor—family, friends, God. My loved ones, cognitive behavioral therapy, and talk therapy have allowed me to restructure my thoughts in a more productive and less destructive way. After all these years of hiding, shrouded in shame, seeking support has allowed me to regain my identity as a person worthy of love and a voice with which to express myself.

Thank you, Ted, for creating such a sacred space, a nonjudgmental dialogue, for self-reflection. Your play is a thing of beauty."

- LILLY

JOEL

"**DEPRESSION, ANXIETY, PTSD,** and self-harm were the story of my life throughout my teenage years and well into my twenties. My world so often felt shrouded by darkness in places where there was supposed to be light. Struggle after struggle, I wrestled to get to the bottom of what was causing all my turmoil. Eventually, I realized I was gay.

For the home-schooled daughter of a Focus on the Family executive, gay was the worst possible thing I could be. It was not only unacceptable, it was an abomination. I was an abomination. Internalized shame kept me in a dark place for far too long.

It wasn't until I finally realized that God loved me exactly the way I was and that I wasn't the disgusting person so many people told me I was that I really found healing and freedom. But it came at a cost. Being authentic and honest about my sexuality cost me nearly everything when I came out of the closet in 2012. I lost my family, I lost my church, I lost my hometown, and I lost many of my friends.

I felt completely abandoned at a time I needed people the most. In my lowest moment, I contemplated suicide. What kept me alive was that odd contradiction that, even when I'd lost almost everything, I found myself happier and freer than I'd ever felt in my life. One day at a time, I pushed myself forward to walk in that authenticity.

While I have found much joy and freedom in my life since then—I now have a wonderful wife, an amazing church family, and two furry babies that make me smile every day—I continue to struggle with emotional scars and the damage that was done in the wake of coming out. PTSD, nightmares, and anxiety still often remind me of the road I've walked and the memories that still travel with me.

I'm so grateful for Ted's play bringing light to the topic of mental illness. His story is needed and carries hope to so many of us."

– AMBER

"I HAVE BEEN IMPACTED by suicidal thoughts and self-destructive behaviors at key stress points in my life. I have mostly understood my life story as a process of recovery. I was misdiagnosed, overmedicated, and poorly counseled for fifteen years. I was hospitalized for suicidal thoughts, anxiety, and depression a week after my thirtieth birthday. In the hospital, I learned that the story I had been telling myself was not true: I was not f**ked up. I was not sick. I was not a series of mental illnesses. I was a person who needed structure, healthy relationships, and a sense of accountability to stay sane through the ups and downs of living.

I have since benefited from a well-grounded counselor who is helping me shape my identity for the first time outside of other people's expectations. I also gain insight and support through a twelve-step program. I now understand that my self-destructive thoughts were largely based on fear and sadness. I am also learning that feeling my feelings is part of my healing journey.

The trauma of growing up in a family that exhibited mental illness has caused the greatest amount of pain in my life, and the only way through the pain has been to feel it, name it, and sit with another person who understands it. I am deeply grateful for what Ted is doing with this tour, and I hope many people come to know themselves through this tour in a new way."

- SCOTT

HERMANN

DEBRA

BRENDA

"I WAS DIAGNOSED with major depression, anxiety, and OCD when I was fifteen. Before then, living my life was like riding a roller coaster while on an acid trip. I had no idea what was going on, and I didn't know how to communicate my feelings, especially while going through puberty with all its crazy emotional changes. At thirteen I'd started cutting myself. First it was little nicks here and there; then I started to like how it felt, because I was feeling something. But someone saw my cuts and told a guidance counselor about them. I was called into the office, but I didn't want to talk. I didn't know there was anything to talk about. What I did know was that I hated myself. I knew I was cloudy in the head, and I hated everything.

My parents had never experienced anything like this before. I was their only child, and they didn't know what to do. We went to a therapist, but that weekend I tried to kill myself. My parents' relationship was falling apart because of me, and I couldn't take it anymore. I was cutting and planned on bleeding out. As I was tearing apart my arm, my alarm clock went off, which was weird, because it was nighttime. The radio came on, and two songs played one after the other: 'Hold On' by Abandon and 'The Valley Song' by Jars of Clay. I heard the lyrics, dropped my blade, and cried. That is when I heard a small voice in my head tell me that I was going to be OK, that I was loved and someone cared. I cried and prayed and cried some more.

Fast forward seven years to today. I lived through two more suicide attempts, more therapists, medication after medication, and countless panic attacks. I am currently two years clean from self-harm, medicated correctly, and have a support group of friends and family who help me along the way. Now I know how to deal with my emotions and what to tell others when something is a trigger. My goal is to help banish the stigma of mental illness. Too many people know too little about these illnesses that are silently killing the ones we love. Few want to talk about them or turn on a light in a dark hallway that can show sufferers the way to the truth. I want to show those people that there is so much more to a person than we think, and we just all need to listen."

– ALICIA

"I SUFFERED from epilepsy and went through brain surgery and now am seizure free. This should have led to total happiness, but then my husband of fifteen years wanted a divorce. It was a bitter time. All of a sudden, I didn't have my husband telling me what to do, when to do it, or how or where. And I found out I did not know how to live without his direction. After many horrible mistakes and failures, I attempted suicide. That provided the biggest lesson ever, as I lost everything and ended up in a group home. I found a way out, but my family sold everything, so now I am homeless. The tears were wasted as I live today with the same things I lost. Just a different color and texture. What I have today will not make me wealthy or poor, but the lessons in learning forgiveness have made me rich. I live today to help others learn forgiveness."

- KAREN

KAITLIN

LAUREN

"I HAVE BEEN TRAUMATIZED psychologically by the aftereffects of a severe traumatic brain injury. Music has saved me. I would never wish this tumultuous experience on anyone. But if you can live again after dying and deal with people's reactions to the changes in you, you can take anything."

- NOAH

"I HAVE HAD on again–off again feelings of depression and hatred toward others as a result of being bullied at school at a young age. People I thought were my friends mocked me and found ways to anger me from second grade to fourth grade, and it was during this time that I questioned the reason for my existence. But where there were bullies, there were also people to support and guide me. It's been a slippery slope for the past eight years, and even in my new school I struggle to feel appreciated. I may have recovered from the worst of it, but the social anxiety I developed has put my patience and joy to the test. It's like my mind is playing tug-of-war: one moment I can be enjoying myself, and the next I feel like everyone is ignoring me. The struggle and pain might completely vanish at times, but there needs to be something to hold on to. If you struggle this way too, remember what you enjoy and the good that people have done for you.

At times I might start losing my peace of mind, but then I remember those who have pushed me back up again and the ambitions I'm still trying to fulfill. I have been blessed with a life that, overall, is much easier than the lives of many others. I refuse to squander what I have now when a young child soldier in poverty can only wish for a taste of a more peaceful life.

The struggle isn't easy and it may always stay with you long after the worst has passed, but there is always someone who cares about you and will support you—don't ever forget that."

- Daniel

JACKIE

"WHEN I WAS EIGHTEEN my father committed suicide. This destroyed everything I thought I knew about life. It made me face depression for the first time. I turned to alcohol, which solved nothing.

Two and a half years later my mother, and best friend, died. My life began to spiral downward. I did not deal with my growing depression and crippling anxiety. I again turned to booze. I totaled my car and got a DUI, got arrested for fighting, lost my nana to a heart attack, lost my pappy to suicide, lost my aunt and godmother to cancer, and then my best friend committed suicide right in front of me.

Attempts to seek counseling were defeated by a new tragedy at every turn. I simply did not have time to mourn the death of one family member before another would die. I was so lost. I continued to use drugs, alcohol, and women to cope. Falling deeper and deeper into despair, I sought help from my doctor. I was diagnosed with severe anxiety, depression, and PTSD.

This solidified what I had already known but kind of made things worse for me. I hid behind my diagnosis to get out of things or make excuses for my actions. I did not listen to the people who were trying to help me. I found myself failing school, broke, with nowhere to go. I had lost so many friends from the paths I took and had no one else.

I decided to kill myself.

I drove myself to my parents' grave with some beer and a razor. I sent a text message to my sister, telling her I loved her, and her response ultimately saved my life. She said how much she still believed in me and that she loved me and wanted to hang out. She wanted to hang out! After all the times I'd messed up and disappointed my family. Love saved my life that day.

So! I stood up, and I started to actively work to better my life. I started to talk about my emotions and have been working very hard to correct the issues I face. It is working! It is now my mission to share what I have learned. Suicide, depression, and anxiety are issues that need to be discussed. Education can be a path to helping and healing."

- JOSH

"I CAME FROM A BROKEN HOME and my father was abusive and cheated on my mother. This really took a toll on me. In my junior year of high school a major injury cost me my dreamed-of football career. Also, I was being emotionally abused by my girlfriend at the time. These challenges brought on serious depression and thoughts of suicide. In my freshman year of college, I actually attempted suicide. I felt very stressed and couldn't take it anymore.

From surviving this experience, I have learned that, no matter what the world throws at you, you can overcome it. I still sometimes battle with my emotions and struggle to control my stress level. But I have found that certain things bring me joy and make me happy. Also I have discovered that talking to God about any troubling feelings brings me peace and helps me get through the rough times."

- ROBERT

"IT'S BEEN SAID that people have four pillars, like a building, holding themselves up. We hear quite a bit about taking care of our physical health. That's only one pillar! If I'm going to live in balance, I must also address the emotional, the spiritual, and the mental pillars. As a child, I grew up physically healthy. Living on a farm, we were very active with chores, and I loved playing with my friends.

In school I excelled academically, but I always had something emotional going on. Usually it stayed beneath the surface. You know the script: 'Hi, how are you?' 'Good.' People don't appreciate it if the answer is regularly a negative one. I felt I had to always be 'good' and 'fine' until well past the point when I was actually 'terrible' and 'lousy.'

So it was that I found myself in high school with an eroded emotional pillar. But what do you do when your center is collapsing, and this instability is leading to your losing control of any ability to reason? Things like panic attacks began, as the physical part of me got tired of trying to compensate for the broken mental and emotional components. I spent a few days in the hospital after one of these attacks, when my heart rate was clearly indicating that things weren't going well. I began seeing a psychiatrist, but there was no talk of bipolar illness. I was given iron pills and a no-sugar diet. I didn't feel crazy yet, but this plan of action was going to help me get there.

Mental illness, which for me was later diagnosed as bipolar disorder, continued eroding my already weakened emotional and mental pillars. I remember getting progressively angrier around age seventeen. I had quit playing team sports, as I just couldn't handle the highs and lows resulting from my play or the game's outcome.

I began living in fear and actively pushing everyone out of my life. But the important thing for you to remember is, you never have to stay stuck where you are. Maybe you need to slow the treadmill of your life and take a break. I needed hospitalizations to get breaks. Maybe you need therapy and/or medication to bring your brain chemistry back into balance. I apparently needed antipsychotic meds, then antidepressants, then a mood stabilizer. Just because you pray for healing doesn't mean you won't need some meds to help with that healing. And you'll probably need to find a good listener. Someone who'll offer you a hug, a shoulder, two ears, and some words of hope, like a heartfelt, 'I believe in you! You're going to be OK!'"

- DAN

"I WAS IMPACTED by mental health challenges from a very young age. In first grade I tried running away from home and met with my school guidance counselor frequently. When something upset me, like an argument between my mom and me, I'd impulsively hold a kitchen knife to my chest. I faced terrible testing anxiety in sixth grade, and in seventh grade I butted heads with my mom big-time and lost my friend group from being overly clingy and obsessive. I attempted suicide in seventh grade with the mind-set that life without me would be better for my ex-friends and family. It was in seventh grade that I was diagnosed with ADHD, depression, and anxiety.

In high school I was involved in a relationship that was toxic for my mental health. I'm a people pleaser, and I tried to make my boyfriend happy as much as possible while ignoring my own happiness and values. When that relationship ended, I thought of jumping in front of a car so his life would be better and not bothered by me.

I spent a week in a mental hospital, and it opened my eyes to how blessed I am. I became closer to God and chose to stay single for a year (and longer). I wanted to use that time to find myself and be myself again. I got an amazing therapist I absolutely love, and she helps me so much. My faith has grown stronger, because I started to put more of my trust in God. Jeremiah 29:11 is my verse. God has a plan for me and for you. He created you and me for a reason and has a purpose for us. Never give up. Have faith and trust in the Lord. He will help you through the toughest times and be there for you through the good times. Just be patient. You and I are worth more than gold and are precious in the eyes of God."

- JAMIE

"EACH MORNING before I got out of bed, I would listen for what my day would hold. I had learned to calculate the climate of the day by the noises I heard outside my room. If there was arguing, I would stay in my bed as long as I could. If there was silence, I would cautiously step into my day, knowing that at any moment there could be an eruption of chaotic emotions.

Much later in life, my parents received the help they needed for their clinical depression. They are now gone, and I am grateful that we all experienced healing over the last years of our life together.

I have traveled a thirty-five-year span of managing my own depression. And that is not easy to do, being in the public eye. Big questions arise for me: How honest can I be about my struggle and still be seen as a credible leader? Can I trust others with my journey? I have been open when the Holy Spirit nudged me to share. Every day is a new day to live authentically and heed the call of God both internally and externally. This year, God gave me the opportunity to shelter a fifteen-year-old who had to leave her home situation due to the mental illness of a parent. I could see the struggle in her, as her journey had once been mine: to be the parent to her ill parent. As this young woman shared her story with me, I heard the cry of my own inner child, and I was able to help them both. I am convinced that God always gives us an opportunity to heal, and out of our healing, He can bring healing to others."

– DENISE

"I HAVE LIVED with clinical depression for over thirty years, which has been hard on me and on my family as well. It has been a long road toward healing and recovery, but it has also been a rewarding experience. Even if someone's progress seems slow, she or he is still moving forward. I never felt that I had a purpose, but with my healing, God has shown me my direction. My passion is to help others with a diagnosis of mental illness and to let them know that there is hope."

- SHERRY

KATHLEEN

OWEN

"MY LIFE ALMOST ENDED during my junior year at university, and it happened so fast, my brain broke. At least, that's how it felt. I was so utterly empty and numb. Who was I then? A straight-A student, always front and center in class, always striving to be the best pupil, best friend, best person. I was known as a cheerful, friendly individual, though my insides were always raw with worry. Anxiety had been a relentless companion since my first day of grade school. I walked a tightrope every day; one bad grade, one person not liking me, and my identity and self-worth would be shattered.

I thought perfectionism would keep me safe from shame and harm, but instead it poisoned my life to the point where I could no longer function. I fell into a deep ravine of major depression, and my entire sense of self fell apart. At the peak of my major depressive episode, I warned everyone in my speech class what a deceitful, fake person I was and then proceeded to walk out. It was the last class I attended.

I became someone who was completely indifferent and cold. I was exploring new ways of being me, with no filter. If it wasn't for the people who rallied around me, I would not be here today. I also recall having a palpable, deep connection with a few students who were going through their personal hell at around the same time. Profound pain and vulnerability birthed profound connection. I will never forget how we, the lost and broken children of God, cried together.

Eight years of medication, counseling, and faith have played no small role in my ongoing recovery. I lived with the diagnosis of bipolar II for three years, then dysthymia. Now that I have been off medication for several years, I like to think that I am free of those heavy labels. Having said that, I still consider myself to be in recovery and deal with the daunting reality that I could 'break' again. As a highly sensitive person, prone to anxiety, I need to protect and love myself, and I've come a long way to try to see that as a sacred duty.

I now know what life can be like without anxiety and depression, and the freedom is blissful. The once-large thorn in my flesh now feels like a tiny splinter. Because of my journey, I know myself better than many people know themselves, and I have a well of compassion for others.

For anyone who would like to argue that depression comes as a result of being spiritually weak, I would beg to differ. Blessed are the mentally weak and broken, for they have been to hell and back. I am a powerful, wounded healer, because I am broken and resilient. The cracks let my light shine through."

- EMI

Mark

SANDI

"**My work environment** spurred on my anxiety and depression. I went to a counselor weekly but never really opened up about my deep feelings of inadequacy. I couldn't confide in anyone. I never felt suicidal, but I experienced a panic attack and simply hated my job. I had to make a change. But my feelings of inadequacy made that hard to carry out. Also, I'd done the same work for twenty-six years, which made any change daunting. Finally, though, things got so bad, I decided to apply for a job elsewhere. It was one of the hardest things I've ever done. Today I have an entirely new attitude about work and life. I'm still taking medication, and I still hide the fact that I have a mental illness from everyone except my husband. Maybe eventually that will change too."

– Babs

"**Depression** is inexplicable.
I know I am loved.
I know I am blessed.
And yet, I struggle.

Understanding that I am not alone has helped me to cope."

– Eliza

ALAHNA

CAROLEE

"MY MOM'S BIPOLAR DISORDER was undiagnosed until the final six months of her life. My family knew what she had, but she refused to recognize it or get treatment. We endured long periods of her depression, sprinkled with manic phases and a total lack of understanding boundaries. She was compelled to be in control of her family and essentially drove us all away by trying to do so. I was once encouraged by a minister after joint counseling to 'sever your toxic relationship, and don't look back.'

There were periods of time (the longest about eighteen months) when I had to limit our contact, but I couldn't leave her because of a mental illness, even one she knew she had but wouldn't seek treatment for. She was still my mom. The last four or five years of her life she seemed to make peace with some issues, and our conversations were a lot more meaningful and less overbearing. It was hard to watch her final days as reality slipped away for her. But with her formal diagnosis, I was finally released from guilt and anger, along with feelings of never measuring up to her standard of perfection. I finally realized that I didn't have to be enough for her, only enough for myself."

- TESA

"I AM AN ADULT WITH ADD. That's not an illness; not even a 'disorder' as 'Attention Deficit Disorder' implies. Neither is it deficient attention. It's more like I'm over attentive to all stimuli. And, it's genetic. We people with ADD are hardwired that way. Perhaps the 'deficit' for us lies in how our 'condition' is handled by others. Until recently, we were seen as flawed. Many people, including therapists, sometimes believe that we need to be 'fixed.' That cannot happen. For me, meds never worked. Early on most professionals categorically denied that ADD could exist in adults, if it existed at all."

- JACK

"I AM A SURVIVOR. My suicide attempt five years ago left me in a coma for five days. All of my organs were failing and my mom was having to decide whether or not to take me off of life support. On the sixth day, before she made the decision, I had come back fully into my body and claimed it. All of my organs healed in 24 hours.

Afterward, it took me a few months of talking to those who wanted to share with me their experience of my near death to fully understand what had happened. I believe it was love that brought me back. I know my soul wrestled with the decision. I had dozens of people praying 24 hours a day for me, at my bedside, singing to me, talking to me, doing healing work with me. God made it possible for me to return here and finish this wonderful, ugly, beautiful, scary, joyful, difficult life. From that day forward the people who loved me unconditionally stayed by my side, loving me through my process, as difficult as it was. Those who would not see me and shamed me, I let go of with love. Those losses are part of my story, a wound and yet a gift. It is difficult for me to share about this episode of my life because many times it makes others uncomfortable. What I want those who love me to know is that there was nothing they could have done to stop what happened from happening. It was part of my journey to go into the darkness. I am a better person because of it. For those who cannot love me because of this part, I want them to know I love myself, I am not ashamed, and I wouldn't change any of it."

- SHANNON

"MENTAL ILLNESS has taught me that the hardest things to do are the most worthwhile steps to moving forward. Things like forgiving small annoyances, trusting others with your fears, and sharing yourself while having others share with you."

- ANONYMOUS

GLENN

KIRK

HOLLY

live your life
life is a gift
nothing you could have done
He is present with
you.

A SCRAP OF PAPER

Laughter Is Sacred Space: Act II, Scene 5

"Not so long ago a woman approached me after a show with a scrap of paper in her hand. She seemed nervous, and the young woman next to her said, 'Just breathe, Mom.'

After taking a deep breath, she said, 'I knew Lee when he was a boy. Four days before he died, my other daughter attempted to take her own life. Please don't think I'm crazy, but this afternoon while summoning the courage to attend this show, I was visited by Lee.'

'Really?' I said.
'Yes and I have a message for you. From him, from Lee.'

She handed me the scrap of paper with what he wanted me to know. There were four lines on it:

> *Live your life.*
> *Life is a gift.*
> *Nothing you could have done.*
> *He is present with you.*

When I read those words, something snapped inside me and I began to cry.

I wept for Lee,
for her,
for the words I needed to hear.

Those words scribbled on a tiny torn scrap of paper are a fulcrum, an instigator toward healing. I now consider my time of healing as pre-scrap paper and post-scrap paper."

CHEYENNE

SHIRLEY

LAUREN

"I WASN'T AWARE that a miasma was permeating my brain. Interesting, when my friends and family tried to talk to me, no words came out of their mouths. Interactions with people became increasingly robotic. I looked at my young daughter and felt nothing; that was when I knew I was deviant. God was not there.

I had bizarre thoughts; I didn't know if they were true or false. I dared not ask anyone; I would be locked away because of my deviancy. Violent obsessions were carefully hidden. It was important I maintained an escape hatch from this pain. I was entirely detached from life.

Being a psychiatrist is not helpful for a person with bipolar illness. Seeking psychiatric treatment and taking medication was not where I thought of going. I spit out a lot of medications; the doctors didn't understand that the problem was the mutant.

I had secrets. A few I gradually confessed; the remainder I withheld. They were shadowed by shame, fear of judgment, and my unwillingness to revisit certain memories.

I am grateful I am alive and that I love deeply and have family and friends who watched over me and would not leave me alone despite my protests. It has been a frightening journey into the dark recesses of my mind, where I was almost lost.

I see clearly now, but sometimes I have nightmares of that torment. They keep me in check. I know that I am the only one who can choose to save my life."

- PATTI

"I HAVE STRUGGLED with anxiety since my early twenties. I first started to notice it when I got overwhelmingly stressed about tests and exams in college. As my anxieties increased, I began having obsessive-compulsive tendencies revolving around the fear of dying. I gave in to these fears and changed my behavior but worked very hard to make sure nobody would notice.

The more I tried to hide it, the worse everything got. When I finally started to open up to my parents, friends, and sister, I was able to identify my feelings, seek professional help, and learn how to live with my fears. It has been a long journey, filled with good and bad therapists, well-meaning friends who are only sometimes helpful, and a loving, supportive family.

As I become a mother, I hope that I can talk openly with my children about mental health. I want them to understand that mental illness is real, and I want to teach them how to help others who are suffering."

- YASI

"My son was diagnosed with bipolar I in 2013. He spent over fifty days in psychiatric hospitals and over sixty days in a mental health rehab facility that year. We had never known someone with a serious mental illness before this experience. It was a difficult year for him and all of our family. We found hope in our church's community group, in worship through music and reading the Bible, and in reading others' stories and speaking with other families living through this illness. The past year was another difficult one for all of us. My son relapsed and spent over forty days in the hospital and the past six months in mental health rehab homes. We will get through this, but we need one another to find hope. We need the church, we need prayer and the Word of God, and we need the fellowship of others who have walked this journey before us. I find strength in good resources and in speaking with others who have a loved one with a mental illness as well."

– Willie

DORA

"No one is exempt."

- Anonymous

"OUR SON JACK DIED at the age of eighteen on August 24, 2014. He was diagnosed with social anxiety almost a year before he died, and it's possible that the stigma of that diagnosis even added to his anxiety. Most of his friends were unaware of this and even commented after his death that he was always the one who helped talk them through their struggles. He ultimately fell from a crane on a construction site at Penn State's campus after an upsetting series of events prompted him to climb to the top. Even if Jack initially climbed the crane with thoughts of ending his life, I'm not convinced that he didn't change his mind and fall. His death was ruled a suicide by the college after the chief coroner reported such, but this was denied by the coroner who actually performed the autopsy. Losing a child is dreadful. I have learned a lot about mental illness and suicide and believe that the surviving loved ones carry the pain that the suicidal person was trying to end for himself. I find hope in other mothers who are grieving a lost child; I meet them in grief support groups where I live and travel. It is important to me to remember that God is coming along on this journey with me, and I believe that, without Him, I could not go on. He is the one with whom I have constant support."

- KC

LONNIE

RACHEL

"WHEN I WAS IN ELEMENTARY SCHOOL I was very angry, and I hated myself, my family, and anyone else that I came into contact with. Feeling an overwhelming sense of being lost and unwanted, I decided that the world, and especially my family, would be better off without me around. I had a plan to just end it all and put everyone out of their misery. It was going to look like an accident so no one would be to blame and everyone would be happy because I wouldn't be around to make their lives miserable anymore.

When I was going through this time, God placed a man in my life who had done drugs and run away from home, dealing with bouts of anger in his life—all things that I was experiencing. He showed me that my life was not that bad and that people cared. He told me about his relationship with Jesus and what a change that had made in his life. To this day he is my 'big brother' and a very special person to me. I was the first person that he had shared his story with, and I will always be grateful for his willingness to be used by God in that moment. A simple yes to God can make all the difference in your life, and being willing to be vulnerable and share your story may seem insignificant to you, but may really reach someone where they are."

- HARMONY

BARRY

KATIE

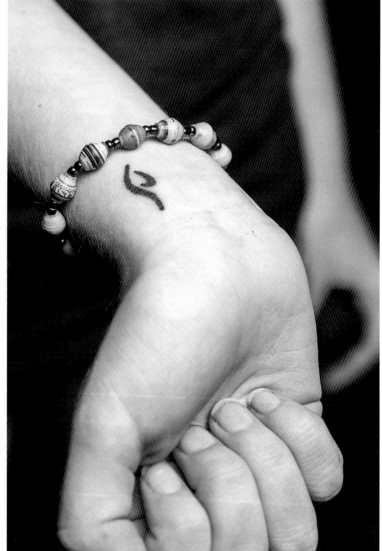

"I HAVE BEEN HOSPITALIZED for suicidal ideations four times over the course of two years. I struggle every day from post-traumatic stress disorder from a sexual assault in the beginning of 2015. I have severe depression, an eating disorder, and generalized anxiety disorder, all in response to that sexual assault. I feel like I lost all of that year to mental illness and trauma, which caused me to look back on my college days with disdain. On the first anniversary of my sexual assault, I had the eating-disorder recovery symbol tattooed on my wrist where I would self-harm. That tattoo has been a symbol of hope and healing for me, and I'm glad I can look at it today."

- AMANDA

"LEE'S SUICIDE WAS VERY PERSONAL to me, as he was one of my neighbors, just across the street and down one house. I was actually mowing our lawn when the ambulance showed up at his home. It wasn't until three and a half years later that I was diagnosed with bipolar disorder and began to feel an even deeper connection with Lee.

I have had two major manic episodes since being diagnosed in 2010. The first was followed by severe depression for about four months, while after the second episode, a few years later, I didn't go quite as low. I have now been stable for almost three years, although those years have not been without smaller ups and downs.

People say I'm doing really well right now, and I am. I have friends, family, a community, a house, a good job, and a vocation that I love. However, sometimes I feel like I'm just waiting for the other shoe to drop, sending me back into the full swing of unmanageable highs and lows.

I find hope in the passage of time, with some sort of stubborn belief that things will turn out all right in the end, or that even if they don't for me, life will still go on."

- LUCAS

KAREN

TATIANNA

"I HAVE SEVERE MAJOR DEPRESSION and I am dealing with multiple physical illnesses. I have a rare disease called Fibromuscular Dysplasia of my renal arteries. March is FMD Awareness Month in the state of Michigan. I always say, be compassionate to others, and just live life the best you can. And always have a smile."

- ANONYMOUS

"MENTAL ILLNESS IS UNPREDICTABLE . . . no one, especially doctors, knows how to deal with it. Just hand out more and more drugs."

- ANONYMOUS

DEAN & MONIKA

"WHEN I WAS TEN YEARS OLD I remember awakening to the panic of my parents, hearing my mother and father say, 'No, there's no way he would do that!' Then my mother came into my room and told me that my sister had called to say that her fiancé, who had been like a brother to me for years, had committed suicide. At the time I did not understand exactly what it all meant, but I knew that Ricky was not in my life anymore. I'd just seen him three days prior. Everything had seemed fine when he visited that weekend, so I soon slipped into denial, then anger, which lasted for years. I would come close to getting into fights with kids for saying 'I should just go kill myself' or argue with my family over chores because I was so angry Ricky was gone.

It was not until I was a sophomore in high school that I finally had closure on his death. I had watched my sister lying on the couch, angry and depressed, for two years, seeing her spiral into drug use and slowly lose the words to speak to us unless it was out of anger. Eventually, she was blessed with a baby, my niece, helping pull her out of that depression.

It seemed that after the night of Ricky's death, the friends I made would always end up telling me that they suffered from depression, and I eventually fell into the role of their caregiver. I love being a resource for people and someone they feel comfortable telling their story to, no matter how 'dark' it might be.

Throughout the years, though, I have had to learn the hard way to become someone who can help her friends in a constructive way and not enable them or fall into the depression with them. Along my journey I have met people who take advantage of the fact that I care about folks struggling with mental illnesses. Although going through those difficult early experiences was challenging, I remind myself that for the most part, I am helping people improve their lives so that their families never have to suffer the heartbreak and mourning that I did for six years.

I love that I am a caregiver. People need help in this world, and I want to be that person for them when they may not have anyone else. Thank you, Ricky; you have given me the brightest path for my future, and everything I do is in honor of you."

– ERICA

ANDREA

ELI

"SUICIDE AFFECTS MANY. The feelings that lead to it should be shared. I attempted it and survived. The results were life-changing."

- KAREN

"WHEN I WAS TWENTY-FIVE I began having difficult bouts of severe depression, and over decades I suffered greatly, with countless therapy sessions, crates of psychiatrist-prescribed drugs, day treatment, and a hospitalization. At fifty, I went into another clinical depression, one that lasted five years. During every previous depression, I had lost hope of ever returning to health, and I once again believed that I would be depressed for the rest of my life.

As before, I made a promise to my husband that I would tell him if I had a plan to kill myself so that he could put me in the hospital. I tried to do art but lost all inspiration by the third year. Then I lost much of my memory. Any travel at all became stressful. Even driving home from the grocery store, I would lose track of where I was and just hope I would recognize my street. But I decided every day, every hour, sometimes every thirty seconds that my life was in God's hands and that I would not take it.

Five years ago, after learning that my daughter and her fiancé (neither of whom had yet graduated from high school) had decided to start their family, I spent a day in the hot sun painting a cottage deck and then took a swim in Lake Chautauqua. Floating on my back, feeling the relief from the prickly, sticky heat, I opened my eyes in time to see the sun emerge from behind a puffy white cloud, and I became aware of a feeling that I hadn't felt for five years and barely recognized: happiness. I was actually feeling happy.

I knew that I had done nothing to produce this lifting of my depression, and I was ready to take heed of several spiritually astute people who had come into my life. Since then, my life has returned to me: art, memory, joy. I am more able now to recognize and catch the early triggers that have always set a downward spiral in motion—negative beliefs and thought patterns (lies) that produce feelings of worthlessness, leading to despair.

I stop and pray. I ask God what He believes about me. I replace lies with God's truth. I do battle against the Humorless One who works to undermine me with his crushing lies. I draw support from people who have God's view of the worth of my life. I spend time with Jesus."

- MILONICA

REBECCA

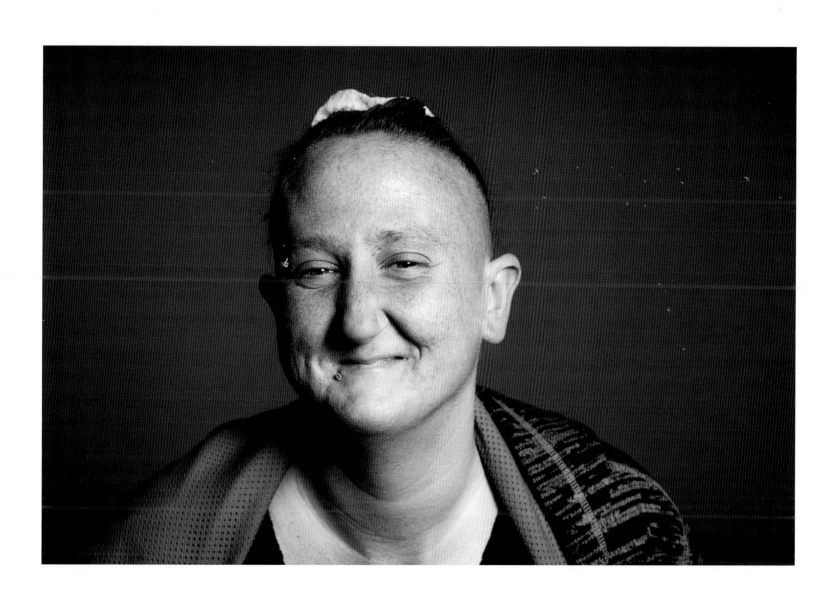

"WHEN I WAS THIRTEEN, I was diagnosed with clinical depression and generalized anxiety disorder. During that time, I struggled with an inner darkness, a war inside of me, an emptiness that was always there, eating away at me. I thought too much and had so many questions about life, the Divine, humanity, existence, consciousness, science, myself, soul, and the unfolding of my inner and outer journey. When I was younger, I had an insatiable desire to know everything, yet I had so many fears about not being who I was supposed to be, about death and about losing my sanity, and about all my repressed pain and anger overtaking me. I was worried about how I looked, how I'd never be good enough for anyone, myself included. I had so much pent-up pain and anger and hurt that the darkness inside of me felt like home. The darkness was familiar; I found a strange comfort in being lost in life. I worried about the future and who I'd become, what I'd do, where I'd live, and if I'd succeed in school or life. I was afraid of being alone, but I have always enjoyed that silence. I wanted to love, but I was afraid of being hurt. I wanted to know truth, while losing sanity was my worst fear. I wanted to live and be happy and free, but I was held down by so much.

I didn't know if there was anything left of me, and I began to question my self-worth. I lost sleep and appetite. I kept to myself mostly and didn't respond with much when asked. I had been living a paradox, and this was my sacred wound. A wound that felt damaging to me but a wound that has also brought healing. Through my struggle with depression and anxiety, I have also learned and experienced an utmost gratitude for life, and I now walk closer with my inner self and with the Divine."

- GARRETT

Josh

BESSA

"MENTAL ILLNESS always affected my life, dealing with major anxiety and depression. I was always told I was just 'having a bad day.' It's real, and it stays with you."

- KENDAL

RUSTY

Leah

"I WORK with academically talented students, many of whom feel that they cannot live up to expectations—their own, their parents', or society's. September is one of the tricky months in their lives as they head back to class with plans for the perfect school year. One of my students has already dropped out. Did I do enough?"

- CARMEN

CARYN

KRIS

"DON'T PRESUME to stereotype people."

- FRED

"My JOURNEY through mental illness began when I was sixteen years old, and through many counseling sessions, it has taught me that, no matter what, I can pull through anything. My mom attempted suicide many times, the last time in 1993. I vowed to myself and God that I would never do anything to harm myself or others."

\- TWILLA

RON

LINDA

NAOMI

"THERE IS NO WAY to really understand the journey of mental illness until you walk with someone daily, all day long, for many months. And even then, you understand only as an observer. But that's a grand gift."

– HELEN

"WHEN I WAS THIRTEEN YEARS OLD I tried to take my life. At first, I told myself it was just an experiment. I didn't really understand the implications. Then my pain seemed to just grow larger as eighth grade wore on, and self-harm became a way to deaden the pain. You see, I was overdosing on meds. Just a little at first, then larger amounts. To this day, I have the word hope carved into my ankle where I was cutting because I just wanted to feel. The day I had decided to end my life, someone found out—a friend who happened to be a police officer. He helped talk me out of it, and then I discovered how many people actually cared about me, that I wasn't really all alone in the crowd. That night, my coach gave me a huge hug and told me, 'Never believe you have no one to turn to; there is always someone. Even someone you just met.'

I still struggle with depression, although I hate to admit it. In college, the dean of students told me on a day I literally had refused to face the world outside my dorm room that, 'Sometimes all you can do is find three things, no matter how insignificant, that went right that day: 1) I awoke, 2) The sun is shining, and 3) There are flowers growing outside.' Now, even when I feel alone in a crowd or feel that there is no good in the day, I remember what has happened, why I exist, and what I hope to do. It is amazing how such small words can make such a great impact."

- ANONYMOUS

Kathy

CHRISTINA

"I HAVE SURVIVED a suicide attempt. I sliced open my artery with a razor sharp knife. I had been in a deep depression for over seven years. As blood began to spray like a fountain, I glanced to the wall and saw a picture of my son. And God showed me the way. Thankfully, an EMS station was around the corner. I cherish the life I have that the Lord saved."

- TREVOR

Destinee

MARY

"**I WALKED OUT OF MY COLLEGE LIBRARY** into a snowy Missouri evening. I was overextended. Too many art classes. Too many papers. I rarely answered my phone but my parents dutifully left voicemails.

'Carrie, it's your parents. We called. You didn't answer. Call us.'

Occasionally, there was a playful dig at how I was avoiding them or a 'does this thing even work!?' But this time, after the reiteration of my caller ID, there was something different. Something not for me.

A long pause, a heavy sigh, and my mom—'I can't believe you would say that. Why would you say that?'

Click.

It didn't make any sense. I stood paralyzed in the cold and listened to the voicemail on repeat, steeling myself for the ending, tears in my eyes. My mom was in the midst of a years-long depression. A depression that took my vibrant, confident mom and turned her into an unrecognizable person. It was terrifying.

My mom, who had told me freshman year to call less so she could write more letters. My mom, who led youth group summer trips. My mom, the librarian who could find every answer in a book. Now she stayed silent on the phone while my dad and I talked our way through college, work, the weather, and the family cat. It had been 18 months since her last letter and it would be two years till the next.

Hundreds of miles and my collegiate overload afforded me the luxury of drowning in color swatches, epistemology, and political strategy. I wasn't around, I couldn't do anything, plus I had my own life and six paintings of a thumb tack to complete.

So I stopped talking about her. I erased 'mom' from my vocabulary. I needed to call my dad. My dad was coming to visit. My dad and I will do that when I am home. It wasn't fair but it was easier. My way of coping with the fact that my mom, as I needed and wanted her, wouldn't be there.

But then there was this voicemail. A peek into a mind that I couldn't understand. A rare flash of emotion. It was a sign of hope. She was still there. She still felt things. I still felt things. For years, I resaved it when my phone threatened to delete it. I listened to it hundreds of times and cried every time. I needed the reminder that she was still my mom, she was still real, and I still cared about her."

- CARRIE

FRED

GWEN

KATIE

AUTUMN

"OTHERS have made up a word ... bipolar. All I know is that I feel things deeply."

- LISA

LYDIA

PAT

"MANIA IS LIKE AN EXHILARATING RIDE to the top of a roller coaster, going over the top into the clouds, and then plummeting, not just to the ground, but into a deep dark hole of depression.

My bipolar diagnosis came after a second episode. My thinking was off the top. When reality hit, I fell into a deep depression, no longer creative, conversational, and cheerful. I gained 100 pounds, due partially to the medication, and because eating was my only pleasure. I didn't want to go anywhere. I hated going to church to be asked 'how are you?' I felt glued to the bed. Over time, the medication and support normalized my behavior.

In 2012 I participated in a bipolar genetic study with the National Institute of Mental Health. To find medications that are more than 'hit or miss,' NIMH is asking for Mennonites and Amish to volunteer as their lineage is pretty clear. I continue to speak publicly about the study, being bipolar, and ways to walk with those who are depressed.

Being bipolar is a life sentence but I am not imprisoned by it. I have embraced treatment, staying on medication as prescribed. My life is much smoother, like a San Francisco trolley with the usual ups and downs."

- BEV

KIMBERLY & AMELIA

CAROL

NANCY

CHARISA

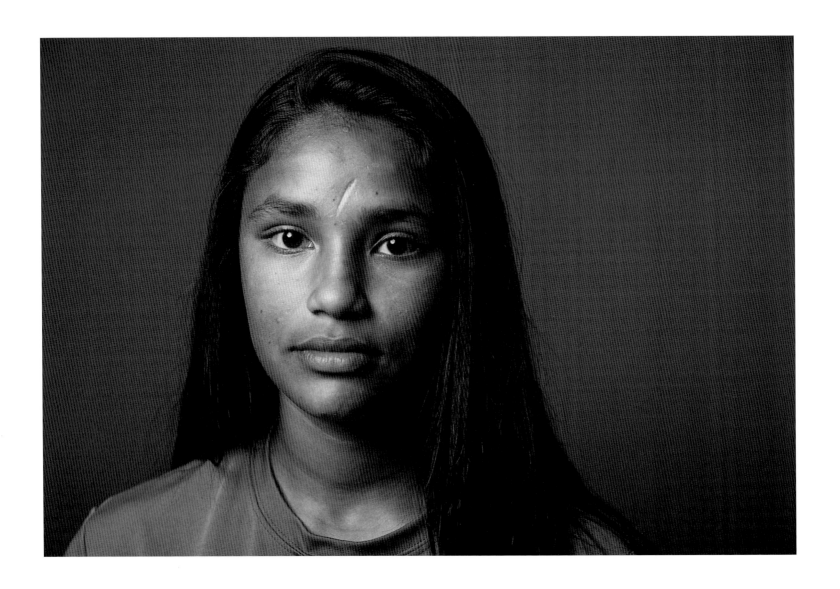

ANNA

"JUST KEEP GOING. No feeling is final."

- ANONYMOUS

IT MUST BE HARD

After a show, in conversations with audience members, a question or observation I often get is, "this must be hard, to experience this again." They mean the loss, the grief, the sense of a missed segment of career . . . a deep "what if." If they have not known me previously, this is the first time experiencing this story, witnessing my real pain.

It is difficult to explain, unless you have been an actor, just how it feels after a show. It feels paradoxical or somehow wrong to try and explain the exhilaration of performing well, of touching our own deep, hard feelings. There is nothing more fulfilling and joyful than spending all of what you possess in the pursuit of art. For the actor, that spending is exposing ourselves, telling the truth of the script, letting the audience see themselves, and assisting in the process of finding empathy for the other. And sharing in laughter.

So when I get those questions I freeze a little, wondering if they would understand my joy of the moment. Occasionally, I will tell what feels like a white lie, and say, "Yes it's hard." But I then have the opportunity to talk of, during the video sequences, my joy of seeing Lee on screen, to remember the warmth of his soul, to remember the feel of his hugs, and yes, even when he pissed me off. I tell them I find myself watching him in a new way each night—damn he was good.

What I want people to feel is the soul of our relationship, not to manipulate their emotions, but rather to give them a glimpse of love. As humans we have great capacity to love, which of course means we have great capacity to feel pain. Pain which doesn't need to cripple us, limit us or keep us from remembering and holding dear the memories of what we were.

Ted and Lee, 2003. *(Photo by Howard Zehr)*

HUMAN FACES
BEHIND THE TOUR

"THE HUMAN FACES TOUR reminded me again of the joy of traveling with great companions on the way to create art. Being on the road with Lee, particularly when he wasn't struggling with depression, was a joy. And off the road, at home, there were two of us who cared deeply about the company. After he died I expected the pain and grief, but part of what I didn't expect: the loneliness of shouldering the business alone. I knew it would be difficult, if not impossible, to resurrect the business, but my new model was to create projects with a variety of writers and actors, and I loved working with other creators, specifically Jeff Raught, Ingrid De Sanctis, and Trent Wagler. But, I could not imagine replacing Lee with another permanent partner. I enjoyed the freedom. I felt unrestrained in the absence of Lee's role of caution toward undertaking new projects. In my grief and unbound imagination, I kept creating shows. Eight shows in the first two years after Lee's death, and ten by the end of three years. All of those shows needed time to develop, time to be rehearsed, and then—here was the greatest weakness—time to be marketed just as robustly and energetically as I had done the creating. I was usually not energized by the marketing.

A phrase I used during that period when I was asked 'how's it going' was 'well, the marketing department is really pissed at the creative development department and they are the same guy.' What I didn't consider was that without having someone who cared as deeply as I did about the life of the entire business, I would be alone in the struggle to keep it going. I was carrying double the load while battling my own grief, and the battle was only headed to an uneasy truce. I stopped volunteering at the high school theater department, stopped coaching baseball, and had no hobbies. There was no time. I could handle the insane schedule, at least for a limited time, but the loneliness . . .

I didn't anticipate the loneliness."

- TED SWARTZ
LEAD ACTOR, PRODUCER, ROAD MANAGER, ASSISTANT LIGHTING TECH,
ROADIE, FATHER FIGURE, ACTUAL FATHER, UNCLE
HUMAN FACES TOUR

"AS THESE FACES AND STORIES ARRIVED in my inbox during and after the Human Faces Tour, I was deeply moved, and sometimes wept, at the honesty, the pain and suffering, and the joy coming through in words and expressions. I felt a sense of unity with the lives of those I only know through this peek into their soul, across distance and differences, through the webs that connect us in this technological era. Their stories intersected with my own. During this same time period, I was feeling a lot of emotional pain and loss brought on by mental health struggles within my own family, and I began to look more intently into the generational history of schizophrenia and other mental disorders, abuse, and addiction that have impacted my family lines down to the present.

I found myself missing my father, who died almost twenty years ago. I've spent enough time in therapy processing how his alcoholism affected me, and have long since forgiven him. Yet, this past year, I've felt a deeper connection to him. After learning more about the abuse and shame he and his sister suffered under the shadow of a father with schizophrenia, who was in and out of mental institutions and jail, I want to tell him that I understand. I understand his need to self-medicate with alcohol. I understand his emotional unavailability and why he would sometimes act out in frightening ways. I want to tell him how my life was, and is, impacted from that same DNA and trauma he suffered. And how it has carried on through the next generation in different ways. And the next. Not to excuse it. But to understand and forgive at yet a deeper level, seeing more clearly the man, his essence, beneath the symptoms. And, I want to tell him that all of the hardship and suffering can be held with love and compassion. That healing can happen, both past and future, and this can change what we pass on to the next generation. I want to tell him how much I love him. While nobody knows what happens after death, I believe our spirits and souls are eternal. In whatever form he exists, I think he already knows and understands my heart.

Being part of the creation of this book has reminded me how connected we humans are with one another, something we don't often recognize. We seldom know the secret struggle of others around us—the losses and pain and joys that have impacted their lives. Yet, the web of our common experiences connects us. Our existence as living beings connects us. And at a deeper level, I believe we are interconnected by the core of love that is what we are at our essence. I am honored to have received and pored through each portrait and story, and I hold profound respect for each one. My prayer is that a ripple effect flows forth from this book, creating space for courageous conversations and new connections not just through our shared pain, but through the compassion and love that holds all things together and heals wounds we can't even see."

- VALERIE LUNA SERRELS
BOOKING AGENT, CO-PRODUCER, ANXIETY WRANGLER
HUMAN FACES TOUR

"TOURS ARE CHAOTIC. We ride in a van all day, worn to a stupor by the rumbling of the road, only to pile out of the vehicle at our destination, pry the Tetris of props and set out of the back, and meet a slew of new people. We fling the set up, wrestle the sound system into submission, and I remind Ted five times to put that prop underwear in your pocket before you forget! I'm running tech, making sure things happen as they ought to. In the hours before curtain, nothing is ever happening according to plan, and I am fretting. Finally, when all is in order, lights dim, and the real work begins.

Onstage, Ted tells his story. Baring his soul to the audience, who have agreed by virtue of attending the play, to open themselves to listen and perhaps be vulnerable themselves. Ted doesn't do all the work, and the audience members are not the only ones who are changed. For an hour, we all breathe together, our souls interwoven. They bring their own experiences of pain and grief, love and thriving, and meet Ted in a swirling chaos of stories.

Then we're back in the van. On to the next show. Digging through the detritus around us for another lunch of Kashi bars and apples.

But we're carrying with us what happened during and after that last show. The van is where we integrate everything we saw and heard, all the bits of their lives the audience shared with us, stories that will live inside our hearts long after the show. It is a place where we talk and laugh and process, a chaotic fermentation vessel for dreams.

There are days on tour you can't even remember what state you're in, much less where you left your pants. When my leg of the tour was done, I realized I'd left a pair of shorts in the van. The next day I received a photo: my shorts hung up in the middle of the jumble of props that make up the cacophonous set of *Laughter Is Sacred Space*.

Something of myself, left behind in the chaos, made part of the show."

- ALISON BROOKINS
TECH CREW, HUMAN FACES TOUR

"BECAUSE OF MY OWN STRUGGLES with anxiety and depression, and with the way mental illness has affected my family, I was glad to join the Human Faces Tour as a sound and stage tech to try to help reach out to others and wash away the stigma surrounding mental illness. I believe that talking honestly about it is the first step to alleviating a lot of the pain it brings. One seldom knows the true struggle of those around us. By being open to the stories of others, and sharing our own, I believe we can help people in ways that were impossible to imagine before."

- DEREK SWARTZ
TECH CREW, HUMAN FACES TOUR

"**I HAVE STRUGGLED WITH DEPRESSION** most of my life, and there were different times when thoughts of suicide crossed my mind. The first time was in fifth grade, then again in high school, and later in college. After a good family friend died by suicide, and seeing the pain, sadness, sorrow, and anger the circumstances of his death had caused, I made a promise to myself that I would never do that to my family. I believe that is a big reason I'm still alive to tell my story today.

In early 2016, I was experiencing another bout of depression that made me question whether at age twenty-seven I had already served my purpose in life. By continuing to live, was I being selfish and wasteful of our planet's limited resources? At the same time, I didn't want to hurt my family. This mental battle caused my brain to break, and I spent the better part of three months barely eating and only having enough energy to watch TV and sleep. At some point during those three months, someone asked my dad and me to make wooden acorns for our church's three-hundredth anniversary celebration. In a moment of clarity, I said yes to helping. On my darkest days, I was okay with ending my life. I had come to the conclusion that my family would, at some point, forgive me, but I thought it was too mean to leave my dad hanging with the acorn project. The acorns kept me going. I told myself that I could not die until they were done. It took a long time for me to get around to finishing those acorns. Thankfully, with the help of therapy, I was able to get back on my feet.

Ted invited me to go on the Human Faces Tour with him in the fall of 2016. I was very anxious but also honored and excited. I liked the idea of the tour. I was nervous to go as I was coming out of the depression and didn't want to mess up the good things that Ted had going. I went along, and that was one of the best decisions I've ever made. It got me out of the house. We laughed more times than I can count. Stories from that tour still make me laugh to this day. I was able to meet people and hear their stories of recovery, which gave me the energy to keep moving forward on my own mental health journey.

On a Sunday in September 2017, my dad and I presented our acorns to the children in front of the congregation. We explained to them that the wood for these acorns came from an oak tree that was alive on the property when the first members of the church gathered in the 1700s. Although the tree had died, the acorns symbolized the ongoing life of our church and the role that each person plays in helping the church grow and flourish. They were part of what caught the eye of a new attender, a young woman, and she became interested in learning more about 'the acorn guy.' And that was the starting point for a casual conversation that eventually led to our marriage in 2019.

From experiencing and getting through depressive episodes, I am more aware of the red flags that alert me to the need to reach out for help. I also now know that it's okay to talk about this chronic illness with the people around me and to recognize and deal openly with its exacerbations."

- DIETRICH ALDERFER
TECH CREW, HUMAN FACES TOUR

Steven, Ted, and Dietrich about to depart for the first leg of the tour. *(Photo by Velma Stauffer)*

Derek, Ted, Alison, and Steven in Goshen, Indiana. *(Photo by Derek's Long Arm)*

MENTAL HEALTH STATISTICS

Suicide is the 2nd leading cause of death for people aged 10–34.
(NIMH. Mental Health Information: Statistics: Suicide)

Approximately 129 Americans die by suicide every day.
(CDC. Data & Statistics: Fatal Injury Report 2017)

Suicide among males is 4 times higher than among females. Male deaths represent 79% of all US suicides.
(CDC. Vital Signs)

The suicide rate for African Americans is 70% lower than that of the non-Hispanic white population.
(US Department of Health and Human Services. Office of Minority Health: Mental Health and African Americans)

Young adults aged 18–25 years had the highest prevalence of any mental illness (25.8%) compared to adults aged 26–49 years (22.2%) and aged 50 and older (13.8%).
(SAMHSA 2017 National Survey on Drug Use and Health)

Depression is the first leading cause of disability worldwide and is a major contributor to the global burden of disease.
(National Center for Biotechnology Information. US National Library of Medicine. National Institutes of Health)

1 in 8 women experience depression in their lifetime; twice the rate as men, regardless of race or ethnic background.
(NAMI. Press-Media Releases 2008)

The suicide rate for veterans aged 18–34 increased from 40.4 suicide deaths per 100,000 population in 2015 to 45 suicide deaths per 100,000 in 2016.
(US Department of Veteran Affairs. VA National Suicide Data Report 2005–2016: Office of Mental Health and Suicide Prevention)

The suicide rate was 1.5 times greater for veterans than for non-veteran adults in 2016, after adjusting for age and gender.
(US Department of Veteran Affairs. VA National Suicide Data Report 2005–2016: Office of Mental Health and Suicide Prevention)

American Indian/Alaska Natives have the highest rates of suicide of any racial/ethnic group in the United States. The rates of suicide in this population have been increasing since 2003.
(CDC. Morbidity and Mortality Weekly Report: March 2, 2018)

Poverty level affects mental health status. Adults aged 26 or older living below the poverty line were almost 2.5 times more likely to experience a serious mental illness than those living above the poverty line.
(SAMHSA National Survey on Drug Use and Health. The CBHSQ Report: November 15, 2016)

In a 2018 survey, 39% of LGBTQ respondents seriously considered attempting suicide in the past 12 months.
(The Trevor Project National Survey on LGBTQ Youth Mental Health 2019)

MENTAL HEALTH RESOURCES

American Foundation for Suicide Prevention (AFSP)
www.afsp.org
888-333-AFSP (2377)
AFSP raises awareness, funds scientific research and provides resources and aid to those affected by suicide.

Anxiety and Depression Association of America (ADAA)
www.adaa.org
240-485-1001
The Anxiety and Depression Association of America (ADAA) is an international non-profit membership organization (with more than 1,800 professional mental health members) and a leader in education, training, and research for anxiety, depression and related disorders.

Centers for Disease Control and Prevention/Mental Health (CDC)
www.cdc.gov/mentalhealth
800-CDC-INFO (800-232-4636)
888-232-6348 TTY
Providing reports and other products that can serve as resources to public health officials and other health professionals who need up-to-date statistics and data sources around mental health and mental illness.

Crisis Text Line
www.crisistextline.org
Text HOME to 741741 for free, 24/7
Every texter is connected with a Crisis Counselor, a real-life human being trained to bring texters from a hot moment to a cool calm through active listening and collaborative problem solving. All of Crisis Text Line's Crisis Counselors are volunteers, donating their time to helping people in crisis.

Depression and Bipolar Support Alliance (DBSA)
www.dbsalliance.org
800-826-3632
DBSA offers in-person and online support groups for people living with a mood disorder as well as friends and family. Parents who have a child living with depression or bipolar can join the online community for parents, the Balanced Mind Parent Network.

National Alliance of Mental Illnesss (NAMI)
www.nami.org
800-950-NAMI M-F, 10 am-6 pm ET
Text "NAMI" to 741741
info@nami.org
NAMI, the National Alliance on Mental Illness, is the nation's largest grassroots mental health organization dedicated to building better lives for the millions of Americans affected by mental illness.

NAMI Faith Net
www.nami.org/namifaithnet
Helpline: 800-950-NAMI
NAMI FaithNet is an interfaith resource network of NAMI members, friends, clergy and congregations of all faith traditions who wish to encourage faith communities who are welcoming and supportive of persons and families living with mental illness.

National Institute of Mental Health (NIMH)
www.nimh.nih.gov
866-615-6464
nimhinfo@nih.gov
The National Institute of Mental Health (NIMH) is the lead federal agency for research on mental disorders.

National Suicide Prevention Lifeline
www.suicidepreventionlifeline.org
800-273-8255
888-628-9454 (Spanish/En Espanol)
800-799-4889 (Deaf & Hard of Hearing)
We can all help prevent suicide. The Lifeline provides 24/7, free and confidential support for people in distress, prevention and crisis resources for you or your loved ones, and best practices for professionals.

OK2TALK.org
www.ok2talk.org
OK2TALK is a community where teens and young adults struggling with mental health conditions can find a safe place to talk about what they're experiencing by sharing their personal stories of recovery, tragedy, struggle or hope. Anyone can add their voice by sharing stories, poems, inspirational quotes, photos, videos, song lyrics and messages of support in a safe, moderated space.

Substance Abuse and Mental Health Service Administration (SAMHSA)
www.samhsa.gov
800-273-TALK (8255) National Suicide Prevention Lifeline
A division of the U.S. Department of Health and Human Services, SAMHSA's mission is to reduce the impact of substance abuse and mental illness on America's communities.

Suicide Awareness Voices of Education (SAVE)
www.save.org
SAVE was one of the nation's first organizations dedicated to the prevention of suicide. Our work is based on the foundation and belief that suicide is preventable and everyone has a role to play in preventing suicide. Through raising public awareness, educating communities, and equipping every person with the right tools, we know we can SAVE lives.

The Trevor Project
www.thetrevorproject.org
866-488-7386
Text START 678678
The Trevor Project is the leading national organization providing crisis intervention and suicide prevention services to lesbian, gay, bisexual, transgender, queer & questioning (LGBTQ) young people under 25.

Veterans Crisis Line
www.veteranscrisisline.net
800-273-8255 and Press 1
Text 838255
The Veterans Crisis Line is a free, confidential resource that's available to anyone, even if you're not registered with VA or enrolled in VA health care. The caring, qualified responders at the Veterans Crisis Line are specially trained and experienced in helping Veterans of all ages and circumstances.

CONTRIBUTOR BIOGRAPHIES

TED SWARTZ is the artistic director and owner of Ted & Company TheaterWorks and the executive director of the Center for Art, Humor & Soul, based in Harrisonburg, Virginia. Both theater and seminary trained, Ted is the creator or co-creator of more than twenty plays, performing primarily across North America for more than twenty-five years, and is the author of the book *Laughter Is Sacred Space*. His loves include his wife, Sue, and their three sons, three daughters-in-law, and five grandchildren. Oh . . . and baseball.

VALERIE LUNA SERRELS is the project director and booking agent for Ted & Company TheaterWorks and the founder and facilitator of Shenandoah Valley Church of the Wild, reconnecting humans with the natural world in an expanded beloved community. She's a card-carrying bibliophile who loves reading, writing, and spending time with trees, bodies of water, and her family—husband Craig, their five incredible grown children, and one fabulous grandson. She and Craig live in Bridgewater, Virginia, with their three cats and many bookshelves. Valerie has a master's degree in Conflict Transformation and Peacebuilding with an emphasis on restorative justice and is a recent graduate of the School of Celtic Consciousness.

STEVEN STAUFFER was born and raised in the three-stoplight town of New Market, Virginia. After studying photography at Eastern Mennonite University and graduating in 2010, he moved to New York City in 2012 for a slight change of pace. There he spends his time taking photos and shooting/editing video across the commercial, documentary, and narrative worlds. He has worked on many projects with Ted Swartz over the years; this book is their first print endeavor. Steven finds that whether a project is a photo shoot or a film, making a human connection with the subjects and audience alike is paramount to creating meaningful work.

TED & COMPANY THEATERWORKS is a touring theater company based in Harrisonburg, Virginia, led by veteran actor and playwright Ted Swartz. Using humor and storytelling to stimulate conversations around issues of faith and social justice, Ted & Company offers live plays, DVDs, digital videos, scripts, discussion guides, and more. The troupe is a team of dynamic actors and musicians who are passionate about creating art that evokes both laughter and reflection.

ACKNOWLEDGMENTS

This book was a slowly evolving process and could not have happened without the big hearts of so many people. Enormous thanks to Steven and Valerie for their passion and artistic sensibilities in making this project what it is:

Steven, for initial vision and the brilliant eye in capturing the faces and shaping the fabulous design. Thank you for being unflaggingly positive and flexible.

Valerie for your doggedness and commitment, infusing the book with your powerful voice, vision and imagination. Truly this book would not have happened without you.

Special thanks to Beth Daugherty for shepherding us through the process and acknowledging the unique challenge of working with three distinct voices to create a coherent final product. Your expertise and positive spirit were exactly what we needed.

Thanks to the crew for the tour: Dietrich Alderfer, Alison Brookins, Josh Kraybill, and Derek Swartz. It was a pleasure to share the laughter, snacks and the wide ranging deep conversations with you. Thanks for your generous adventuresome spirit. The Human Faces Tour remains my favorite tour ever, in large part due to your presence.

Thanks to the careful eye and creative minds of the PowderHorse Writer's Group: Jim Clemens, Jennifer Murch, Valerie Luna Serrels (co-author), Shirley Showalter, and Carolyn Yoder. Thanks to fellow writer and artist Michelle Milne, and our other readers Tina Burkholder, Janet Daugherty, John Leonard, and Rachel Martin Swartz for their astute feedback.

Appreciation to Jim Clemens for using your particular and sometimes peculiar skill set in proofreading, and special thanks to copyeditor Leslie Kazanjian.

Many thanks to Eric Chu Siu Keung of Pimlico Book International (Crystal Asia Network Ltd) for his patience and Pimlico's expert printing; and Steven Bloom for his guidance.

As always, Sue Swartz, thanks for your critical eye, love, grace and support through yet another project. I cannot imagine doing this creative life without you.

- TED SWARTZ

PORTRAITS FROM THE HUMAN FACES TOUR
Mental Health Struggles and Resilience

Unless noted below, photographs by Steven Stauffer

Photograph on page 4 courtesy of Wayne Gehman
Photograph on page 173 courtesy of Howard Zehr
Photograph on page 186 courtesy of Velma Stauffer
Photograph on page 187 courtesy of Derek Swartz

Book design: Steven Stauffer

First edition, 2020

Printed and bound in China by Pimlico Book International

ISBN-13: 978-0-578-55924-7
Library of Congress Control Number: 2019912231

Ted & Company TheaterWorks
PO Box 33
Harrisonburg, VA 22803
www.tedandcompany.com

Cover design and photos: Steven Stauffer

Front cover portraits: Dan (top), Emi (bottom)
Back cover portraits: Naomi (top), Daniel (bottom)